C000258905

Royal Doulton Series Ware

Volume 3 Doulton in
the Nursery
Children's Stories
Games and Pastimes
Nursery Rhymes
Miniatures

LOUISE IRVINE

RICHARD DENNIS
London 1986

ROYAL DOULTON SERIES WARE

Design and Phototypsetting by Flaydemouse
Edited by Arwen Warmer
Photography by Colin Jeffrey Associates and
Prudence Cuming Associates
Printed in Great Britain by Edwin Snell printers
Published and distributed by Richard Dennis
144 Kensington Church Street, London W8

ISBN 0 903685 17 5

© 1986 Text Louise Irvine, photographs Richard Dennis
and Royal Doulton Limited

RD
October 1986

Front cover: pattern book drawing for
Into the land of dreams series
Back cover: Neil Faulkner's artwork for
The Snowman collection

Acknowledgements

I am deeply indebted to Royal Doulton Limited
for permission to reproduce material from their
archives, and for their generous co-operation in
the preparation of this book.

I should like to thank the author, Louise Irvine, for
her particular dedication and expertise.

Additional thanks are due to Tessa Chester, Tony
Cross, J. Cunliffe, Desmond Eyles, Sharon Goodchild,
Michael Heseltine, John Jenkins, Jocelyn Lukins,
Stephen Nunn, Diane Peterson, Doug Pinchin,
Caroline Rees, J. Rickett and P. Taylor.

RD
September 1986

Contents

Introduction to Volume 3

Doulton in the Nursery

This book is the third on the subject of Series ware, the name applied to an assortment of decorative and practical items, such as plates, vases and jugs, which are printed with popular imagery. Volume One was concerned with series inspired by literature, historical events and popular illustrators. Volume Two recorded all the series depicting "olde worlde" imagery. This volume continues the study by investigating Royal Doulton's contribution to the nursery. Successive generations of children in many parts of the world have been weaned on baby plates and mugs from the Burslem Pottery. It is ironic that these pieces, which were once given to junior to bash up and down on the high chair, should become collectable but that is now the case with many of the nursery wares featured in this book.

Royal Doulton's interest in the nursery dates from the late Victorian period when there was increased awareness of the specific needs of children. The various health and education acts of the 1870s finally established that society had certain obligations towards young people. No longer were they expected to be miniature adults as childhood was recognised as a very important stage in life. The consumer potential of the child grew with this new status and was further developed by a new gift giving occasion, the Victorian celebration of Christmas. Toy manufacturers vied with each other to produce increasingly sophisticated playthings. Publishers began to specialise in children's titles which aimed to entertain rather than "improve" as their predecessors had done. Potteries also abandoned the didactic imagery which had featured on earlier children's mugs and plates and designed tablewares with subject matter that would appeal to young audiences; for example, nursery rhymes and fairy tales.

Potters had been supplying nursery equipment since the eighteenth century when pewter and silver feeding bottles were replaced with the more hygienic ceramic versions. Doulton's Lambeth Pottery continued the tradition of assisting nursing mothers and, as well as feeders, provided water filters decorated with toytown motifs and cot-sized stoneware hot water bottles inscribed "Baby". During the Edwardian era, the Lambeth artists specialised in designing tile murals depicting nursery rhymes and fairy tales for the entertainment of young invalids confined to hospital and these picturesque panels had a profound influence on the nursery tableware designers at Doulton's pottery in Stoke-on-Trent.

When Henry Doulton took over the Pinder Bourne factory in Burslem in 1882 he inherited several nursery ware designs which he kept in production for several years. The earliest appears to be a little girl and boy in eighteenth century costume with the inscriptions *Le Mouchoir Retrouvé* and *Bonjour M'sieur Le Marquis*. There was also a large legacy of transfer printed designs featuring images of children at play and adults at leisure. Whilst not designed specifically for the nursery, these scenes come within the scope of this book as they give insight into the life of the Victorian child. This is also true of the *Aesthetic Style Children* and *Maidens* series and the distinctive *Blue Children* collection, all of which feature in the *Games and Pastimes* section. These scenes, which are reminiscent of the engravings in ladies' and children's periodicals at the turn of the century, admirably illustrate how children and young adults dressed at this time. No longer were little girls and boys kitted out in costumes identical to those worn by their parents. It was recognised that they needed freedom of movement to enjoy their recently accepted state of childhood and so restrictive corsets and hampering layers of petticoats were abolished. However, they were still required to wear hats or bonnets at all times out of doors, even when playing.

Stoneware baby hot water bottle made at Lambeth c 1910.

Baby mug featuring a duck 1935–1942.

Tile murals featuring nursery rhymes designed by Margaret Thompson for St Thomas's Hospital.

Many of their games are still enjoyed by children today, an exception being the rolling of hoops which was primarily a Victorian preoccupation. Although some of the Doulton scenes of children at play were produced for doting parents or grandparents, others were clearly intended for the nursery. The first plates and mugs in the *Pastimes* series were inscribed with popular proverbs such as "Joys shared with others are more than enjoyed" or "It takes two to make a quarrel". Children were obviously expected to digest these words of wisdom along with their porridge but it is significant that the proverbs were soon deleted and the series appears to have been more successful without them.

By the opening years of the twentieth century children expected to be entertained at mealtimes, not lectured. Charles Noke, who pioneered Royal Doulton Series wares certainly seems to have borne this in mind when commissioning designs for his younger

Pinder Bourne
design inherited
by Doulton
depicting little
girls cooking
turtle soup.

Pinder Bourne nursery designs *Le Mouchoir Retrouvé* and *Bonjour M'sieur Le Marquis* inherited by Doulton and produced until 1913.

Pattern book featuring Pinder Bourne design.

Pinder Bourne designs inherited by Doulton and produced by them from 1882.

Pinder Bourne designs inherited by Doulton and produced by them from 1882.

Pinder Bourne designs inherited by Doulton and produced by them from 1882.

audience. His first great success was a collection of nursery rhymes and fairy tales designed by Royal Academy exhibitor, William Savage Cooper, which first appeared on fine bone china tableware in 1903. These nursery rhymes were still sufficiently popular in the 1930s to warrant a revival on a new collection of earthenware shapes, in the latest style.

Nursery rhymes continued to be Doulton's staple diet for toddlers' teatimes until the outbreak of World War Two. However, by that time they were already being usurped by the phenomenally popular *Bunnykins* ware which had been introduced in 1934. This playful rabbit family created by a young nun, Barbara Vernon, is still a favourite with children today. Indeed, *Bunnykins* ware has become so collectable that there is a separate specialist book on the subject, *The Bunnykins Collectors Book*.

Bunnykins ware.

The Bunnykins success story owes a lot to the age-old fascination of anthropomorphic creatures. When an animal is depicted with human attributes the result is often appealing and highly amusing. In such a form, even the intense moralising of Aesop's fables becomes acceptable to young readers and before such books were written expressly for children, they pored over their parents' copies. Animals who can speak and who wear the fashions of the day also abound in *Alice's Adventures in Wonderland*, one of the greatest stories written for children. The *White Rabbit*, the *Dormouse*, the *Mock Turtle* and the *Blue Caterpillar* all feature on Doulton's exquisite bone china teaset which is ideal for any tea party (mad or not!). Animal fantasies such as these have been a constant feature of Doulton's nursery designs and reflect the personal interests of Charles Noke who delighted in dressing up animals in human clothing for the HN figures collection. In the *Children's Stories* section, Lewis Baumer's dancing pigs, A. B. Payne's comical cartoon characters Pip, Squeak and Wilfred, Jill Barklem's Brambly Hedge mice and Christina Thwaites's new interpretations of the heroes from *Wind in the Willows* are all descendants of Aesop's fabulous bestiary.

Over the years several famous children's book illustrators have been linked with Doulton's nursery wares. Today's artists, such as Jill Barklem and Raymond Briggs of *Snowman* fame, have been consulted frequently about the adaptation of their drawings but arrangements in the past are not so clear. In the case of Lewis Baumer, who was a prolific contributor to Punch and other periodicals as well as a much sought after book illustrator, it was possible to purchase lithographic sheets of his humorous drawings from the Eagle Transfer Works, a potteries print supplier. It may be that Royal Doulton did not go ahead with their original plans to launch his designs after seeing the same images reproduced by a competitor on a nursery ewer and basin. Certainly no Doulton examples have yet come to light although the pattern books indicate that several items were designed.

Also elusive are the teapots and biscuit boxes which featured Randolph Caldecott's' illustrations for *My Pretty Maid*, first published in 1882 in one of his famous picture books. Engraved and printed by Edmund Evans and published by George Routledge or Ward Lock, these sixpenny toy books transformed children's libraries. They were profusely illustrated using distinct outlines, filled in with even washes of the subtlest pastel shades, an effect which was accurately reproduced by Evans's coloured wood engravings. Such illustrations were easily translated into the "print and tint" technique employed in the decoration of Series ware where the outline is created with a transfer print from an engraved copper plate and the colouring is later applied by hand.

Randolph Caldecott's work had a profound influence on Doulton Series wares (also see Volumes 1 and 2) as did Edmund Evans's other close associate, Kate Greenaway. If Randolph Caldecott can be dubbed the "Lord of the Nursery" then Miss Greenaway must surely be the Queen for her impact on children's lives was not confined only to their books but spread to their china and even to their costume. Children during the "Aesthetic" period of the 1880s and '90s were dressed in her distinctive high waisted dresses and mob caps. There are Greenaway style figures galore in Series wares, the Doulton artists' way of paying homage to this remarkable talent.

Original illustrations from *Under the Window* by Kate Greenaway.

See Pastimes 18.

Christening mug with violet motif 1912.

Personalised baby mugs in popular patterns introduced 1934 and withdrawn during World War 2.

Not all illustrators are so easily identified on the nursery wares – the problem being that the most successful had many imitators, thus clouding the issue. The style of Ann Anderson, for example, can be detected in *Nursery Rhymes* L but Agnes Richardson, H. G. C. Marsh-Lambert and others all worked in the same vein making positive identification difficult. To complicate matters further, Charles Noke had a facility for working in many different styles depending on the subject and often resorted to well known publications for inspiration.

Noke was continually searching for new ideas for the nursery until the outbreak of war in 1914. Thereafter, life styles changed – families became smaller and the elaborate ritual of the nursery tea began to disappear so there was not such a demand for forty piece children's teasets in a variety of designs. Instead, each child had his own plate and mug, sometimes personalised. From 1934 until World War Two, a few of the favourite nursery designs featured popular children's names. The pattern books record two different nursery rhyme series with the names Rose and William and a scene of cats and mice with the name Joan but no doubt other designs and names would have been available. Personalised mugs were made prior to this but they seem to have been commissioned as christening mugs and feature initials and dates as in the violets design inscribed "MOG 1912". For a more expensive christening gift it was possible to buy the most popular fine bone china nursery patterns accessorised with silver handles and spoons and presentation boxed. These occasionally come on the market, often unused and so in pristine condition.

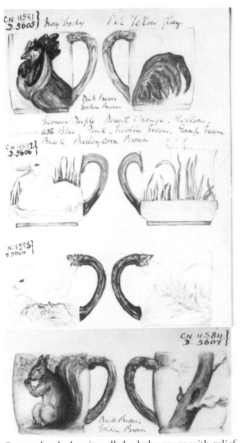

Presentation boxed gift set of *Nursery Rhymes L.*

Pattern book showing all the baby mugs with relief decoration of animals introduced in 1935 and withdrawn by 1942.

Pattern book pages depicting two baby's plates introduced in 1913 and withdrawn by 1955.

Baby's plate with yacht and windmill designs.

Baby's plate in *Willow* pattern.

Generally speaking, though, few complete sets survive the rough and tumble of nursery life. In fact it seems incredible that any of the fragile bone china pieces have stood the test of time. Edwardian children must have been on their best behaviour at mealtimes. Babies, however, cannot be relied upon to observe good table manners and so special weighted plates were designed with exceptionally thick sides to withstand all attempts to hurl them off the high chair. Many of these still survive intact – the only damage having been inflicted by metal spoons scraping away at the image. This was usually a standard nursery pattern or an adopted adult tableware design such as the *Willow* or *Windmill* scenes illustrated here.

After World War Two, the only nursery ware still in production was the ever-popular *Bunnykins* and this remained the state of affairs until the 1980s when Jill Barklem's *Brambly Hedge* illustrations were tentatively introduced on a collection of four wall plates. These appealed to both the young and the young at heart and were equally at home in a child's bedroom as in the family lounge. Gradually beakers, cups and saucers, teapots, sugar bowls and cream jugs were added and thus the principles of Series ware were revived. The *Snowman* collection, which has also been hugely successful, introduced yet more novel shapes; money banks, musical boxes and mobiles and these have quickly become popular seasonal fillers for the Christmas stocking.

Royal Doulton first celebrated Christmas in the early 1900s when they promoted miniature vases and jugs depicting Santa Claus as a substitute for cards. It is not known how long this craze for china Christmas greetings lasted but they certainly did not usurp the traditional card market. Undeterred, Doulton continued to offer tiny pieces to the growing number of miniature collectors and varied the subject matter to include most of the popular patterns. To date nearly fifty different series have been recorded in miniature so even if space is at a premium it is possible to enjoy a comprehensive collection in the confines of one china cabinet. It helps, however, to have a healthy bank balance, for these tiny treasures can be more expensive than their standard sized counterparts. Series ware generally, has become much sought after in recent years but the subject is so vast that there is still plenty of scope for collectors. In this volume alone there are more than fifty different series to look out for – so happy hunting!

A selection of Blue Children rack plates.

A group of miniatures. *Top to bottom, left to right:* Coaching Days, Shakespeare, Welsh, Zunday Zmocks, Dickens, Under the Greenwood Tree, Fruit Tree, Arabs and Camels, Gallant Fishers, Blue Iris, Lincoln Imp, Christmas Fare, All Black Cricketers, Silhouettes, Venice, Skating, Bateman's Smug Golfer, Sunset Scene, Historic Towns – Guildford, All Black Cricketers, Fisherfolk, Hunting, Dutch, Snowflake, Nursery Rhymes – Little Bo Peep, Norfolk, Cock and Hen, Willow Pattern, Bobbie Burns, Rabbits, Dutch, Welsh, Bobbie Burns.

How to use this book

The series in this volume are divided into four sections: Children's Stories; Games and Pastimes; Nursery Rhymes and Miniatures. Each series, except the Nursery Rhymes series which appear in chronological order, is listed alphabetically within the section under its correct title if known, otherwise its most common title. When the exact title is not known, the series can be located with reference to the index which lists names of characters featured or quotations and inscriptions.

After some brief introductory remarks on the subject matter covered in each section, the information on each series is entered under several headings for easy reference.

SCENES/TITLES
In each series the number of different scenes depicted can range from one to more than forty. When the exact title of the scene is known it has been recorded, otherwise a description of the image is given to aid identification.

CHARACTERS
Some series such as *Baumer's Rhymes* have this additional heading where all the different figure poses recorded are described.

PATTERN NUMBERS
All the D, E or H numbers so far recorded for each series are listed together. Sometimes one pattern number can refer to the entire series, for example, D3119 is the *Springtime* series. In this case the pattern number can be a useful aid for tracing more items in the series. More often, however, each series has several different pattern numbers which denote the use of varying colourways, borders or shapes. The date of introduction of each design is indicated by the pattern number. See the *Date Guide* on page 109.

BORDERS
When a pattern was produced with more than one border, the variations are listed under this heading. For example, *Tobogganing* has two borders so far recorded; Fir tree and Greek key with stylised flowers. Whenever possible border variants have been illustrated.

COLOURWAYS
The majority of Doulton Series ware decoration is polychrome but any other variations are also listed such as blue and white, sepia, or green and white. When unusual glaze effects or bodies are recorded these are also listed, for example Holbein glaze, a rich yellow effect; Whieldon ware, a rather coarse earthenware, or Celadon ware, glazed a subtle green.

SHAPES
An enormous variety of shapes were used in the Series ware range. Under this heading an indication is given of the extent of each series and the types of shapes employed for that pattern. By consulting the *Shape Guide* in Volume One, collectors may become familiar with the most common vase numbers and shape names. Many items are not illustrated in the shape guide, in particular the diverse bone china shapes and specially moulded items.

DATES
The introduction and withdrawal dates are given when they are recorded. Pattern numbers are a useful guide to dating in conjunction with the *Pattern and Code Number Guide (Date Guide)* on page 109.

DESIGNER
The designer's name is given when it is known, but this is rarely the case.

SPECIAL BACKSTAMP
In addition to the Royal Doulton trademark some series had their own specially designed backstamp. Some examples are given below.

The information for this book has been gleaned from surviving Doulton pattern books and from major collections. Although this is the most comprehensive study on Series ware produced so far it cannot claim to be complete. Some of Doulton's records are missing and with them, no doubt, further details of Series ware scenes, pattern numbers, glaze effects and so on. It is hoped that collectors will inform us of any additional material they discover in order that future studies will be more complete.

Series ware backstamps.

Children's Stories

Few books were written expressly for children before the eighteenth century and the earliest tended to be moralistic and improving. Young readers preferred to raid their parents' libraries for books such as Malory's *Morte D'Arthur*, Bunyan's *Pilgrim's Progress* and later, Defoe's *Robinson Crusoe* and Swift's *Gulliver's Travels*. Many of the essential ingredients for children's enjoyment were to be found in these pages, adventure, heroism, even giants and monsters but not in an easily digestible form and so most of these tales have since been edited for juvenile consumption.

Children have also been avid readers of fairy tales which again were originally intended for adult entertainment, handed down by word of mouth from one generation to the next until they were finally recorded for posterity by Charles Perrault in 1697, the Brothers Grimm in 1812 and Hans Christian Andersen in 1835. Surprisingly, *Little Red Riding Hood* from Perrault's original collection is the only fairy tale to have been depicted as a Doulton nursery series although the *Mermaids* series may well have been inspired by the popularity of *The Little Mermaid* by Hans Andersen. However, fairies or more specifically pixies and gnomes do appear on a few popular patterns – the most appealing seem to have been influenced by Arthur Rackham's illustrations for *Peter Pan in Kensington Gardens* written by J. M. Barrie.

A new path in imaginative children's literature was opened up in 1865 with the publication of Lewis Carroll's *Alice's Adventures in Wonderland*. This was not the normal didactic tale previously considered appropriate for children but pure fantasy and entertainment which provided Charles Noke with the basis for a hugely popular nursery ware set, introduced in 1905 and not withdrawn until 1932. The timeless quality of many Victorian and Edwardian children's classics has encouraged many subsequent artistic interpretations. Recently Christina Thwaites, a young illustrator of children's books, was commissioned by Royal Doulton to design a series of plates depicting

incidents from Kenneth Grahame's *Wind in the Willows* which was first published in 1908.

It is not necessary to probe the past for inspiration as there is much of merit being produced for children today. One of the most exceptional talents in recent years is Raymond Briggs who, since 1957, has been a full time illustrator and author, mainly of children's books. *The Snowman* is probably his best known work as it was adapted for television in 1982. Three years later Royal Doulton launched their *Snowman* gift collection which was an immediate runaway success.

An equally enthusiastic reception was given to Jill Barklem's *Brambly Hedge* mice when they first appeared on Royal Doulton wall plates in 1983. Since then many different shapes featuring more scenes and characters from her *Brambly Hedge* stories have been regularly added to the collection. The appeal of Jill Barklem's illustrations lies in her charming characterisation of the little fieldmice and their intricately detailed habitats. Endowing animals with human characteristics has a long and popular tradition in children's literature and this in turn is reflected in Doulton Series ware. In 1927, plates, cups and saucers were decorated with the exploits of a very famous anthropomorphic trio; Pip, Squeak and Wilfred. Pip the dog, Squeak the penguin and Wilfred the rabbit had starring roles in a strip cartoon which ran from 1919 until 1955 in *The Daily Mirror* newspaper. Created by B. J. Lamb (Uncle Dick) and drawn by A. B. Payne, these mischievous animals had a thriving fan club called the Wilfredian League of Gugnuncs so called because "Gug" and "Nunc" for "Uncle" were the only words which young Wilfred could utter. The trio appeared in many guises besides china, for example, in Christmas annuals, on greetings cards and as chocolate models.

Time has obscured the origins of the other anthropomorphic creatures in this section, the *Motoring Cats and Dogs*. No doubt there is a fascinating story behind their frenetic activities but it has proved elusive to date. Motoring also inspired the limerick portrayed early this century on a Royal Doulton mug and plate. These facetious jingles date back to the early nineteenth century but they were popularised in 1846 by the publication of Edward Lear's *Book of Nonsense* which is still avidly read by children today.

A jingle or verse is the surest way of capturing a child's attention and many poems written for adults have been adopted by them. Blake's *Songs of Innocence* (1798) were not so much poems for children as visions of the world seen through childlike eyes. Many of the simplest verses now appear in anthologies for young readers including *The Piper* which was portrayed by Doulton in 1917. Two years later Stoddard King's poem *The Long, Long Trail*, which was popularised as a song during the Great War, was the inspiration for one of the most attractive Doulton designs *Into the Land of Dreams* and it is featured on the cover of this book.

Alice in Wonderland

SCENES/TITLES

1 Alice and the Duchess – 'Tut, tut child' said the Duchess, 'everything's got a moral if you can only find it'
2 Alice and the Dormouse – 'They lived on treacle' said the Dormouse after thinking a minute or two
3 Alice and the Caterpillar – 'Repeat You are old Father William' said the Caterpillar
4 The King and the Hatter – 'You must remember' remarked the King 'or I'll have you executed'
5 The Mock Turtle – 'Once' said the Mock Turtle with a deep sigh, 'I was a real turtle'
6 The Three Gardeners – 'Look out now Five, don't go splashing paint all over me like that'
7 Alice and the Queen – 'Off with her head' the Queen shouted at the top of her voice
8 Alice and the Rabbit – 'Run home' said the Rabbit 'and fetch me a pair of gloves and a fan'
9 The Dormouse – 'Once upon a time there were three little sisters' the Dormouse began in a great hurry
10 The Queen – 'Get to your places' shouted the Queen in a voice of thunder
11 The Two Footmen – 'From the Queen an invitation for the Duchess to play croquet'

12 The Blue Caterpillar – 'Well, I should like to be a little larger, sir,' said Alice 'three inches is such a wretched height to be'
This scene is the same as number 3 but with a different quotation
13 The King – 'Don't be impertinent' said the King 'a cat may look at a King' said Alice
14 The Mad Hatter (standing)
15 The Mad Hatter (seated)
16 Father William and the Youth
17 Father William (standing on head)
18 The White Rabbit
19 The Duchess

PATTERN NUMBERS
D2863, D2883, D5180, E4021, E4090, E5180, E5187

COLOURWAYS
Polychrome

SHAPES
Rack plates, Rheims teacup and saucer, Burke beaker, bread and butter plate, Bedford sugar and cream, oatmeal saucer, bowl, baby plate, miniature jugs

Alice in Wonderland. Plate 12.

Alice in Wonderland. Cups, saucers and miniature jug, *left to right* 7, 19, 4, 14, 8, 18, 16.

Alice in Wonderland. Teaset, *left to right* 2, 1, 6, 3, 5.

DATES
This series was introduced in 1906 and
withdrawn by 1932

Note Alice in Wonderland by Lewis Carroll was
first published in 1865 and has been
acknowledged as one of the greatest children's
stories ever written

Alice in Wonderland. Catalogue page, oatmeal saucer features 15, beaker features 17.

21

Alice in Wonderland. Plates, *top to bottom* 13, 10, 9, 11.

Babes In The Wood

This design appears in the pattern book c. 1900 and the printing plate was destroyed in 1955. As yet no pieces have been recorded giving details of pattern numbers.

Babes in the Wood. Pattern book.

Baumer's Rhymes

SCENES/TITLES

1 'Just see them poor little girls
   A reading of their books
   I'm sure they must be French or Greek
   So very sad they looks'
2 'Well did you ever see such airs
   That silly little doggy wears'
3 'Remember Piggy when you dance
   To move with ease and grace'
4 'Now children don't be reckless please
   But keep quite close to me
   You cannot be too careful
   When you're bathing in the sea'

CHARACTERS

1 Pigs staring over wall at girls and school mistress
2 Dogs watching girl and dog
3 Girl dancing with pig
4 Pigs on the beach
5 Pigs cycling
6 Pigs, little girl and gnome reading
7 Gnomes reading
8 Girl with dolls in class
9 Girl with walking toys
10 Pig yawning at pig playing trumpet

PATTERN NUMBERS
D3509, D3904, D3919, E7324

BORDERS
Scroll and flower

COLOURWAYS
Polychrome

SHAPES
Baby plate, teacup, Flagon toilet set

DATES
This series was introduced in 1911 and
withdrawn by 1930

DESIGNER
After designs by Lewis C. E. Baumer for his
book of moralistic rhymes entitled *Jumbles –
A Toy Book* (1897)

Baumer's Rhymes.
Left, from top to bottom
8, 1, 2, 5, 9, *right,*
from top to bottom 1,
6, 7, 3, 4, 3, 10,

Baumer's Rhymes.
Teacup 4, baby
plate 3.

Brambly Hedge A. Plate.

Brambly Hedge A
SCENES/TITLES
Midwinter's Eve

BORDERS
Holly and mistletoe

COLOURWAYS
Polychrome

DATES
This plate was issued in 1983 and was exclusive to Lawleys by Post customers until March 1984

DESIGNER
After designs by Jill Barklem for her Brambly Hedge book *The Secret Staircase* (1983)

CHARACTERS
Additional characters feature on the smaller shapes such as the thimbles and pendants; Mrs Apple, Basil in the rushes, Clover toasting bread, Lady Woodmouse, Little Children, Primrose sleeping, the Wedding and Wilfred playing a whistle. Fourteen of the characters have also been modelled as figures

BORDERS
Seasonal fruit, flowers and foliage

COLOURWAYS
Polychrome

SHAPES
Wall plates, beakers, teacups and saucers, teaplates, teapot, sugar and cream, thimbles and pendants

DATES
This series was introduced in 1983 and new shapes have been added in subsequent years. It is all current with the exception of the pendants which were withdrawn in 1985

DESIGNER
After designs by Jill Barklem for the covers of her *Four Seasons* Brambly Hedge books (1980)

SPECIAL BACKSTAMP on wall plates featuring appropriate quotations from the books for each scene

Brambly Hedge B – Four Seasons
SCENES/TITLES
1 Spring
2 Summer
3 Autumn
4 Winter
5 Spring Story Tea Party
6 Dusty Dogwood with a batch of buns

Brambly Hedge © Jill Barklem 1982
Licensed by Copyrights

Brambly Hedge Books
published by William Collins and Co. Ltd.

Brambly Hedge B – Four Seasons. Milk jug, sugar bowl and teapot, *left to right* 6, 5.

Brambly Hedge B – Four Seasons.
Teacups, saucers and plates, *left to right,
from top to bottom* 1, 2, 3, 4.

Brambly Hedge C – Interiors. Plates, *left to right* 3, 1, 4, 2.

Brambly Hedge C – Interiors
SCENES/TITLES
1 The Dairy
2 Old Oak Palace
3 The Store Stump
4 Crabapple Cottage

BORDERS
Fruit and flowers

COLOURWAYS
Polychrome

SHAPES
Wall plates

DATES
The set of four plates was introduced in 1986 and is still current

DESIGNER
After designs by Jill Barklem in the *Four Seasons* Brambly Hedge stories

SPECIAL BACKSTAMP featuring appropriate quotations from the books for each scene

Brambly Hedge D – Midwinter's Eve
SCENES/TITLES
1 The Snow Ball
2 The Discovery
3 Candlelight Supper
4 The Entertainment

BORDERS
Holly and mistletoe

COLOURWAYS
Polychrome

SHAPES
Wall plates

DATES
This series of four plates was introduced annually from 1984 onwards

DESIGNER
After designs by Jill Barklem from her Brambly Hedge books *The Secret Staircase* and *The Winter Story*

SPECIAL BACKSTAMP featuring appropriate quotations from the books for each scene

Brambly Hedge D – Midwinter's Eve. Plates, *left to right, top* 1, 2 *bottom* 4, 3.

Gnomes A

SCENES/TITLES
1 Gnome bowing to fairy
2 Two gnomes smoking on toadstools
3 Gnome talking to rabbit

PATTERN NUMBERS
D2876, D2885, D3212

BORDERS
Scroll and shell

COLOURWAYS
Polychrome

SHAPES
Rack plates, Flagon toilet set, baby plate

DATES
This series was introduced in 1907 and
withdrawn by 1919

Gnomes A. Plate, 3.

27

Gnomes A. Rack plate, 1.

Gnomes A. Flagon jug, 2.

Gnomes B

SCENES/TITLES
1 Tree trunk with six gnomes peeping out from roots
2 Tree trunk with five gnomes amongst roots, one in foreground
3 Tree trunk with three gnomes amongst roots
4 Tree trunk with six gnomes amongst roots behind mushrooms
5 Three gnomes behind mushrooms

PATTERN NUMBERS
D4697, D4899, D5066

COLOURWAYS
Polychrome, with and without gilded cobwebs and other details

SHAPES
Rack plates, Westcott jug, Harlech cup and saucer, Westcott teapot, Joan teaset, Leeds fruit bowl

DATES
This series was introduced in 1927 and withdrawn by 1950

DESIGNER
Charles Noke inspired by Arthur Rackham's illustrations for *Peter Pan in Kensington Gardens* 1906

Note This series is also known as "Munchkins" in the USA

Gnomes B. 2.

Gnomes B. Rack plate and jug, *left to right* 1, 3.

Gnomes B. *Top* 4, *bottom* 5.

Top to bottom, left to right: Alice in Wonderland, Nursery Rhymes A, Nursery Rhymes L, Pip, Squeak and Wilfred, Nursery Rhymes L, Pastimes, Nursery Rhymes F, Tobogganing A, Springtime, Nursery Rhymes F, Gnomes B, Nursery Rhymes F.

Top to bottom, left to right: Gnomes B jug, Alice in Wonderland bowl and jug, Into the Land of Dreams jug, Nursery Rhymes A jug, biscuit casket and teapot, Pastimes teapot, Seaside jug, Nursery Rhymes A beaker, Nursery Rhymes G jug and baby plate, Nursery Rhymes L mug, Pastimes jug.

Into the Land of Dreams. Basin, *left to right* 6, 5, 4.

Into the Land of Dreams

SCENES/TITLES
1 Two children, one with toy horse
2 Two children, one with doll, in front of
  procession of children
3 Two children hand in hand
4 Two children, head and shoulders view
5 Procession of children, back view
6 Back view of girl

PATTERN NUMBERS
D4114, D4484

BORDERS
Stylised landscapes

COLOURWAYS
Polychrome

SHAPES
Vase, Lagoon toilet set, chamber pot

DATES
This series was introduced in 1919 and
withdrawn by 1932

Note The title of this series is taken from a
poem by Stoddard King (1889–1933) which was
popularised as a song during the First
World War
  'There's a long, long trail a winding
  Into the land of my dreams
  The long, long trail'

Into the Land of Dreams. Ewer, *left to right* 1, 2, 3.

Legends

1 Medieval princess playing lyre with cherub
  attendants
2 Man and two maidens with laurel wreaths
3 Man and maiden with flowers
4 Weeping maiden with lyre

PATTERN NUMBERS
D1775, D1785, D1786, D1828, D1830, D1831

BORDERS
Stylised laurel leaves

COLOURWAYS
Whieldon, green, blue and white, Holbein

SHAPES
Umbrella stand, Regent flower bowl

DATES
This series was introduced in 1903 and
withdrawn by World War I

Legends. 3 and 4.

Legends. Flower bowl, 1.

Legends. Flower bowl, 2.

Little Red Riding Hood. *Left to right, top* 3, 2, *bottom* 4, 2.

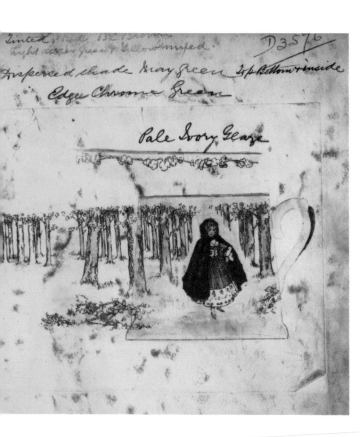

Little Red Riding Hood.
Mug, 1.

Little Red Riding Hood
SCENES/TITLES
1 Little Red Riding Hood in the woods
2 Little Red Riding Hood knocking on
  Granny's door
3 The wolf in bed
4 Little Red Riding Hood leaving home

PATTERN NUMBERS
D3576

COLOURWAYS
Polychrome

SHAPES
Children's mugs

DATES
This series was introduced in 1912 and
withdrawn by 1930

Note This fairy tale was first published in *Contes
de ma Mère L'Oye* (1697) by Charles Perrault

Mermaids

CHARACTERS
Seventeen different mermaids and children
swimming in seaweed

PATTERN NUMBERS
D802, D1015, D1018, D1019, D1221, D1222,
D1223, D1463

COLOURWAYS
Whieldon, blue and white, turquoise, green

SHAPES
Tavern jug, Armada jug, screw top jars

DATES
This series was introduced in 1901 and
withdrawn by World War I

Note Mermaids feature in several children's
stories, the most famous being Hans Andersen's
The Little Mermaid (1836)

Mermaids. Pattern book.

Mermaids. Jug.

Mermaids. Pattern book.

Motoring A – Limerick

SCENES/TITLES
The Wise Motorist with limerick on reverse
'There was a young man of Dacota
Who went to get wed in a motor
Said he to his bride
My horse is inside
We prepare for events in Dacota'

PATTERN NUMBERS
E3247

COLOURWAYS
Polychrome

SHAPES
Rack plates, mug

DATES
This series was introduced in 1905 and
withdrawn by 1914

Motoring Limerick. Mug.

Motoring B – Cats and Dogs

SCENES/TITLES
1 Car full of cats and dogs dressed in human clothes, chased by dogs
2 Car crash with policeman
3 Cat falling out of car, caught by dogs
4 Dog forcing cats out of car

PATTERN NUMBERS
D2433, D2434

BORDERS
Fruit and swag, intertwining ribbon

COLOURWAYS
Polychrome

SHAPES
Rack plates, Tavern jug

DATES
This series was introduced in 1905 and withdrawn by 1934

Motoring Cats and Dogs. Jug, 3 *below* 4.

Motoring Cats and Dogs. Rack plates, *left to right* 1, 2.

Pip, Squeak and Wilfred

SCENES/TITLES
1 "We sing this song for we all belong" –
Squeak and Pip
2 "Goodbye Dear. I hope you find them at
home" – Squeak "So long Wilf! Be back to
lunch?" – Pip
3 "What is it Wilfred? Don't hold on to my bag
like that!" – Squeak "Nunc" – Wilf "He wants
a penny I expect Squeak" – Pip
4 "Hullo Popski and Auntie going to join the
Gugnuncs?" – Gook Nooski "Mmm" –
Auntie
5 "Oh Dear isn't this an ancient pier Pip" –
Squeak "Yes, Be careful how you walk Wilf" –
Pip

CHARACTERS
Some of the characters were also modelled as
figures.

PATTERN NUMBERS
D4692, D4741, D4752, D4753, H3485

COLOURWAYS
Polychrome, sepia, blue and green

SHAPES
Harlech cups and saucers, Empire cup and
saucer, teaplates, baby bowl, mug

DATES
This series was introduced in 1927 and
withdrawn by 1935

DESIGNER
This series was based on the comic strip in *The
Daily Mirror* which ran from 1919 until 1955 and
featured Pip the dog, Squeak the penguin and
Wilfred the rabbit created by B. J. Lamb (Uncle
Dick) and drawn by A. B. Payne.

Pip, Squeak and Wilfred cartoon from their Christmas annual.

Pip, Squeak and Wilfred. Cups and saucer, *left to right* 1, 2, 1.

Pip, Squeak and Wilfred. Mugs and plate, *left to right* 4, 3, 4.

Pip, Squeak and Wilfred. Plate, 5.

Piping down the Valleys Wild
SCENES/TITLES
1 Boy playing pipes 'Piping down the valleys wild'
2 Lambs gambolling 'Piping songs of pleasant glee'
3 Woman with shepherd's crook

PATTERN NUMBERS
D4077

BORDERS
Leaf and tendril

COLOURWAYS
Polychrome

SHAPES
Rack plates, Octagon toilet set and chamber pot, round salad bowl, ice jug, spittoon, fern pot, candlestick number 7227, York sandwich tray, Octagon teaset, Marcella tobacco jar, vase number 7537, Ancestor ashtray, Hecla tobacco jar, Ball tobacco jar, Leeds fruit bowl, oatmeal saucer, trinket set

DATES
This series was introduced in 1917 and withdrawn by 1940

Note This series was inspired by a verse from *Songs of Innocence* (1789) by William Blake
"Piping down the valleys wild,
Piping songs of pleasant glee,
On a cloud I saw a child,
And he laughing said to me:

'Pipe a song about a Lamb!'
So I piped with merry cheer.
'Piper, pipe that song again;'
So I piped: he wept to hear."

Pixies. Baby plate.

Pixies
SCENES/TITLES
Three pixies with lanterns

PATTERN NUMBERS
D3690, D3747

COLOURWAYS
Polychrome

SHAPES
Baby plate, Concord jug, Breda jug

DATES
This series was introduced in 1913 and withdrawn by 1930

Piping down the Valleys Wild. Rack plate, 1.

Piping down the Valleys Wild. *Centre* 2, *above* 1 and 3.

The Snowman
SCENES/TITLES
1 Walking in the Air
2 Snowman Christmas Cake
3 Dance of the Snowman
4 The Party
5 Playful Snowman
6 Building the Snowman
7 Highland Fling
8 Balloons
9 Snowman Band
10 Partytime
11 James and the Snowman dancing

Snowman. Teaplate, cup and saucer, 10, 11.

Snowman. Plate 3.

CHARACTERS
Seven of the Snowman characters have been modelled as figures

BORDERS
Snowmen

COLOURWAYS
Polychrome

SHAPES
Wall plates, teacups, saucers, teaplates, money bank, trinket boxes and musical boxes. Also specially designed 'Build a Snowman' breakfast and eggcup sets and a mobile

DATES
This series was introduced in 1985 and is still current

DESIGNER
After designs by Raymond Briggs for his book *The Snowman* (1979)

SPECIAL BACKSTAMP

© Snowman Enterprises Ltd 1985
Licenced by Copyrights

The Snowman by Raymond Briggs published by Hamish Hamilton

Snowman. Plates,
left to right 1, 2.

42

Snowman. Beakers, *left to right* 1, 4, 5, 6.

Snowman. Mobile, trinket boxes, money bank and musical box, *left to right* 8, 9, 7.

Wind in the Willows. Plates, *left to right, top* 1 and 2, *bottom* 3 and 4.

The Wind in the Willows
SCENES/TITLES
1 Badger's House
2 Preparation for the Boating Season
3 Ratty and Mole go Boating
4 Rambling in the Wild Wood

COLOURWAYS
Polychrome

SHAPES
Wall plates

DATES
This series was introduced in 1984 and is
exclusive to Lawleys by post customers

DESIGNER
Christina Thwaites inspired by Kenneth
Grahame's children's classic *The Wind in the
Willows* (1908)

SPECIAL BACKSTAMP featuring appropriate
quotations from the book for each scene

Games and Pastimes

Play, which had formerly been considered mere idleness, was viewed by the Victorians as a healthy activity. In the days of large families and huge households, children could play to their heart's content in the nursery under the watchful eye of nanny. There were hobby horses, dolls' houses and other toys for private amusement but with so many brothers and sisters around there was lots of scope for group games such as "Blind Man's Buff" or "Musical Chairs". Fifty-three such games were played by Kate Greenaway's exemplary children in her *Book of Games* published in 1889. There were no tantrums or tears, cheating or pushing from her immaculately dressed characters in their pinafores, mob caps or straw boaters. This book and others, in particular Miss Greenaway's first publication *Under the Window* (1878), had a tremendous influence on children's china. Many manufacturers appropriated her designs for nursery tablewares. Wedgwood called their Greenaway style wares *Playmates*, Brownfields called theirs *Pastimes* as did Royal Doulton. Only a few characters in the forty-six scenes which make up the Royal Doulton *Pastimes* series can be matched exactly with Miss Greenaway's drawings but even the most cursory glance through her books leaves no doubts as to the importance of her influence.

Flying kites, skipping, fishing and rolling hoops are just some of the popular pursuits which feature on her pages and in several of the Royal Doulton series. Hoops were very popular with Victorian children and boys had specially manufactured iron ones which clattered along the cobbled streets whilst girls and delicate children had more manageable wooden versions. For the more adventurous a ride on one of the new pennyfarthing bicycles was an exciting proposition though it often ended in a tumble and tears.

Most favourite entertainments would take place in the open air so children particularly welcomed the advent of Spring and often took part in the traditional rituals. Mayday was celebrated with music and dancing with garlands, culminating in the choice of the Queen of the May and these delightful ceremonies are featured in the Doulton series *Springtime* and *Music and Dance*.

The simplest pleasures are often still the most popular and children have an endless capacity to amuse themselves for hours with few or even no props. Picking flowers, making daisy chains, playing piggy-back, scotch horses or hide and seek are just a few of the activities to be seen in the *Blue Children* and *Pastimes* series. Picnics are also a great treat for the little ones particularly at the seaside. Victorian and Edwardian families flocked to the new resorts where the beaches were an ideal playground for the young and several Doulton series show girls and boys engrossed in building sand castles, paddling or shrimping.

In winter the snow is as appealing as the sand in summer and children will play for hours in the icy wonderland. Seemingly immune to the cold they build snowmen or get up to high jinks tobogganing on the slopes as illustrated in the Doulton series *Tobogganing*.

Traditionally boys take part in the more energetic games such as football and cricket whilst the girls play with their dolls and prams. In modern thinking these are sexist stereotypes but this role playing was re-inforced by the Victorians and Edwardians and is clearly illustrated on the nursery china of the time. Little girls were not allowed to neglect the highly valued female accomplishments and would spend dull winter afternoons knitting or practising their embroidery stitches on samplers which would later be framed to display their sewing skills. One of Doulton's most attractive series simulates the cross-stitch effect of a sampler in a delightful pastoral scene featuring a play or Wendy house, as they are sometimes known, which probably explains the alternative title for the series, *Peter Pan*.

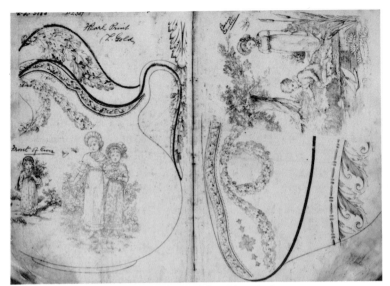

Aesthetic Style Children. Ewer and basin, *left to right* 2, 5, 6.

Aesthetic Style Children. *Left to right, top* 10, 7, *bottom* 12, 9, 8, 11.

Aesthetic Style Children.
Left to right, from top to bottom
1, 2, 3, 4.

Aesthetic Style Maidens. Teapot, 8.

Aesthetic Style Children
SCENES/TITLES
1 Girl feeding birds
2 Girl with branches of berries
3 Boy and girl with rabbit
4 Girl blowing bubbles
5 Girls with fruit arm in arm
6 Boy sailing boat, girl with flowers
7 Three girls with nest of eggs
8 Boy fishing
9 Girl at water's edge picking flowers
10 Girl holding on to the branch of a tree
11 Girl with bare feet picking flowers
12 Girl holding a jug

PATTERN NUMBERS
D1586, D2337

COLOURWAYS
Pink, sepia

SHAPES
Flagon, unrecorded ewer and basin

DATES
This series was introduced c 1890 and
withdrawn by World War I

Aesthetic Style Maidens
SCENES/TITLES
1 Maiden crossing stream on stepping stones
2 Maiden carrying a basket of flowers and
  holding skirts
3 Girl at the seaside
4 Maiden picking berries
5 Maiden shading her eyes
6 Maiden reading to her dog
7 Maiden resting on a wall
8 Maiden with parasol
9 Maiden sitting on a log with wooden pail
10 Maiden feeding dog
11 Maiden resting on a fence
12 Maiden with basket of flowers, birds in sky
13 Maiden reading on a fence

PATTERN NUMBERS
D1039

COLOURWAYS
Polychrome, orange and black

SHAPES
Rack plates, unrecorded teapot

DATES
This series was introduced c 1890 and
withdrawn by World War I

47

Aesthetic Style Maidens. Rack plates, *top* 5, *bottom left to right* 2, 11.

Aesthetic Style Maidens. *Left to right* 4, 3.

Aesthetic Style Maidens. *Top* 6, *bottom* 7.

Aesthetic Style Maidens. *Top* 10, *bottom* 9.

Aesthetic Style Maidens. *Left to right, top* 13, 1,
bottom 12.

Blue Children. 8.

Blue Children

SCENES/TITLES
1 Girl flying kite with dog
2 Girl with basket
3 Girl with baby crying
4 Girl giving piggy-back to little boy
5 Two boys talking
6 Two girls draping daisy chains round a dog's neck
7 Woman sheltering child with cloak in snowstorm
8 Woman playing guitar
9 Woman with muff in snowstorm
10 Woman by seashore
11 Two girls sheltering under umbrella
12 Boy and girl peeping into tree hole
13 Girl with doll talking to a frog
14 Two girls talking to a tiny witch
15 Girl rummaging in mother's basket
16 Woman with child holding cloak
17 Hide and seek
18 Picnic
19 Two girls cross-legged under tree
20 Girl gathering flowers in a basket
21 Three girls watching Tinkerbell
22 Two boys and girl with ball (no photograph available)
23 Eighteenth century girl curtseying to boy
24 Eighteenth century boy doffing hat

PATTERN NUMBERS
D407, D417, D509, D539, D848, D949, D963, D1680, D2161, D4256

BORDERS
Gilded and stylised flowers

COLOURWAYS
Blue and white

SHAPES
Rack plates, oval and round plaques, Gower umbrella stand, Aubrey toilet set, Sheriton toilet set, Carlton fern pot, Bamboo flower pot, Breda jug, Chatsworth jug, Arno jug, Corinth jug, Ball teapot, McVitie and Price biscuit jar, Regent biscuit jar, jardinière and pedestal, various vases

DATES
This series was introduced in the 1890s, augmented in 1915 and discontinued by 1930

Blue Children. Oval plaques, *left to right* 16, 7.

Blue Children. Rack plates, *left to right, top* 2, 12, 13, *below* 17, 14, 21.

Blue Children. Biscuit jar, 1.

Blue Children. Vase, 18.

DESIGNER
Although mostly printed, the scenes had additional background detail painted by hand. Occasionally the artists responsible signed their work although this practice seems to have ceased by 1902. The following signatures have been recorded, J. Boulton, M. Brown, P. Curnock, C. Jackson, F. Jones, Kelsall, A. E. Simpson, Yomans (sic)

Blue Children. Vases and plaque, *left to right* 9, 11, 20.

Blue Children. Rack plates, *left to right* 10, 15.

Blue Children. Biscuit jar, 5.

Blue Children. Vase, 19.

Blue Children. Biscuit jar, 4.

Blue Children. Mug, 24.

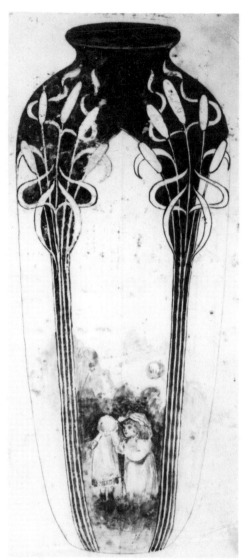

Blue Children. Vase, 3.

Blue Children. Plaque, 6.

Blue Children. Mug, 23.

Cricketers – The All Black Team

SCENES/TITLES
1 'There's style'
2 'Good for fifty'
3 'Out for a duck'
4 'Ready for chances'
5 'Next man in'
6 'I wasn't ready'
7 'The Boss'

PATTERN NUMBERS
D2864, E4336

BORDERS
Foliage

SHAPES
Rack plates, Burke beaker, Clayton jug, Cecil mug, Elsa teacup and saucer, spittoon, loving cup number 7058, Lennox flower bowl, Breda jug, Carlton bowl, Breda teapot, Virginia tobacco jar, china vase numbers 767, 772, 1023 and 1079, unrecorded candlesticks, unrecorded stein, miniature jugs and vases

DATES
This series was introduced in 1906 and withdrawn by 1930

Cricketers – The All Black Team. Plate and miniatures, *left to right* 3, 6, 1, 4.

Cricketers – The All Black Team. Jug, 2.

Cricketers – The All Black Team. Plate 5.

Cricketers – The All Black Team. Plate, 7.

Cricketers – The All Black Team. Catalogue page.

Dancing Piccaninnies. *Left to right* 2, 3, 1, 5, 6, 4.

Dancing Piccaninnies. Teapot, *left to right* 1, 3, 2.

Dancing Piccaninnies

CHARACTERS
1 Girl holding skirt with one hand
2 Girl with hands in air
3 Boy with sun hat
4 Boy with leg kicked up in air
5 Boy wearing hat with hands in air
6 Girl wearing hat holding skirt

PATTERN NUMBERS
D2929, D3976

BORDERS
Pine cones

COLOURWAYS
Polychrome

SHAPES
Pekoe teapot, unrecorded vase

DATES
This series was introduced in 1908, revived after
World War I and withdrawn by 1928

Let's Pretend. Flower bowl, 2.

Let's Pretend
SCENES/TITLES
1 'England's Defenders'
2 'HMS Lark'
3 'Opposition gives opinion strength'

CHARACTERS
1 Boy with tommy gun
2 Sailor waving handkerchief to girl
3 Footballers

PATTERN NUMBERS
D1962, D2828

BORDERS
Townscape, laurel

COLOURWAYS
Polychrome

SHAPES
Toilet set, Regent bowl, child's beaker

Let's Pretend. Mug, 3.

DATES
This series was introduced in 1904 and withdrawn by 1930

DESIGNER
J. Ogden

Let's Pretend. Jug, 1.

Music and Dance. Tobacco jars, *top* A, *below* B.

Music and Dance A

SCENES/TITLES
Frieze of girls and toddlers dancing,
background of trees and grape vines

PATTERN NUMBERS
D227, D328, D398, D410, D1230

BORDERS
Leaves

COLOURWAYS
Polychrome, green and brown

SHAPES
Aston bowl, tobacco jar

DATES
This series was introduced in 1900 and
withdrawn by World War I

Music and Dance C. Flower bowl, 6.

Music and Dance C. *Left to right* 3, 4, 1.

Music and Dance B

SCENES/TITLES
Frieze of girls dancing with garlands of flowers against background of fruit trees and birds

PATTERN NUMBERS
D228, D229, D330, D331, D397, D399, D400, D411, D441, D479, D543, D545, D632, D735, D746, D774, D816, D819, D1243, D1250, D1255, D1731, D1777

BORDERS
Leaves, stylised vine

COLOURWAYS
Polychrome, blue and white, sepia, green and brown, red and brown, Holbein

SHAPES
Round salad, Aston biscuit jar, Dublin biscuit jar, unrecorded jar and lid, tobacco jar, oval salad, Cantor biscuit jar, unrecorded jug, salad bowl, spittoon, Castle jug

DATES
This series was introduced in 1900 and withdrawn by World War I

DESIGNER
A. Peirce

Music and Dance C.
Top 5, *bottom* 2.

Music and Dance C

SCENES/TITLES
1 Girls with tambourines and dancers
2 Girls with lyres and dancers
3 Girls with harps and dancers
4 Girls with violins and dancers
5 Girls with pipes and dancers
6 Girls with lutes and dancers

PATTERN NUMBERS
D327, D328, D329, D372, D423, D424, D449,
D508, D544, D679, D686, D687, D688, D689,
D711, D713, D751, D777, D1013, D1018,
D1023, D1034, D1035, D1049, D1050, D1053,
D1062, D1068, D1069, D1096, D1149, D1167,
D1214, D1225, D1236, D1237, D1238, D1240,
D1241, D1256, D1264, D1384, D1417, D1433,
D1435, D1467, D1711, D1732, D1747, D2055,
D2062, D2132, D2443, D2444, D2490

BORDERS
Gold flowers, chrysanthemums, trellis fruit,
stylised leaves, grape vine, vertical stripes, Greek
key, Morrissian flowers

COLOURWAYS
Polychrome, blue and white, red and brown,
Whieldon, green and sepia, green and white

SHAPES
Rack plate, Croxden biscuit jar, Tudor jug,
Stroon jug, Breda teapot, Lennox flower bowl,
Regent bowl, Virginia tobacco jar

DATES
This series was introduced in 1900 and
withdrawn by World War I

Note Sometimes girls appear alone in a
cartouche on a jug or vase or else the dancers
appear without the musicians

Pastimes. 15.

Pastimes. Rack plates, *top to bottom* 22,
42, 20, 34.

Pastimes. Teapot and jug, *left to right* 3, 17.

Pastimes

SCENES/TITLES

1 Lacrosse and tennis scene – 'East or west, home is best'
2 Boy looking over wall, boy and girl sitting on grass – 'He who takes a child by the hand takes a mother by the heart'
3 Girl looking over wall at ducks – 'A thing of beauty is a joy for ever'
4 Baby playing with toys – 'Little things are great to little men'
5 Boy in field with sheep – 'He has enough who is content'
6 Shuttlecock game with spectators – 'One false move may lose the game'
7 Girl and boy blowing bubbles – 'A word once out flies anywhere'
8 Boy and girl watching others play shuttlecock – 'A little neglect may breed great mischief'
9 Children flying kite – 'When the wind is high the kite will fly'
10 Children playing hide and seek in hay ricks – 'Better go back than go wrong'
11 Boy giving a flower to girl behind fence – 'Love grows with obstacles'
12 Girls making sand pies – 'It's an ill wind that leaves nobody good'
13 Girl giving out fruit on beach – 'Joys shared with others are more than enjoyed'
14 Girl skipping, boy and girl watching – 'Be slow in choosing but slower in changing'
15 Girls watching boat at sea – 'A little leak will find a great ship'
16 Children netting butterflies – 'A good hope is better than a bad possession'
17 Boys playing Scotch horses – 'A rough colt may make the best horse'
18 Boy playing horn for girl – 'He is idle who might be better employed'
19 Five children beside a fence – 'Good words without deeds are but rushes and seeds'
20 Boy on pennyfarthing and spectators – 'Anytime means no time'
21 Boys and girls rolling hoops – 'Let a child have its way and it will not cry'
22 Children on seesaw – 'A friend is worth all the hazards we can run'
23 Boys digging in sands – 'Little and often make a heap in time'
24 Boy and girl mending a kite – 'Advice is easier than helping'
25 Boys playing with hoops, one falling – 'Most haste worst speed'
26 Tennis game – 'Fair and softly goes far'
27 Boy falling off pennyfarthing – 'Haste trips up its own heels'
28 Girl pulling a cart with boy inside –'Precepts may lead but examples draw'
29 Boy and girl with captured butterfly – 'It takes two to make a quarrel'
30 Boy falling off seesaw – 'A false balance is not good'
31 Boy painting plate – 'Always at it wins the day'
32 Boy in boat fishing – 'There's as good fish in the sea as ever came out'
33 Children raking hay – 'Make your hay while the sun doth shine'
34 Boy painting girl's portrait – 'Employment brings enjoyment'
35 Boy and girl with nest – 'A bird in the hand is worth two in the bush'
36 Girls arm in arm on log watching skipping – 'The highest art is artlessness'
37 Girls blowing bubbles
38 Boy and girl building a sandcastle
39 Girls making a daisy chain

Pastimes. Jug, mug and porridge plate, *left to right* 16, 27, 18.

Pastimes. Porridge plate, 11.

Pastimes. Teapot, 2.

40 Girls arm in arm on log, one turning head
41 Girls playing shuttlecock
42 Boy and girl fishing on a fence
43 Boy pointing in distance. girl beside him
44 Girl and boy dancing
45 Two girls arm in arm, walking away from
   girl with basket and baby
46 Baby with parrot and toys
47 Girl with doll

PATTERN NUMBERS
D1216, D1217, D1244, D1506, D1507, D1508,
D1515, D1516, D2122, D2123, D2124, D2125,
D2222, D2223, D2226, D2328, D2391, D2394,
D2546, D2821, D3065, D3452, D3829, D4222,
E232

BORDERS
Fruit and swag, stylised flower, rose, gold
flowers, dog rose, ivy, hearts, Japanese, plain
green

COLOURWAYS
Polychrome, blue and white

SHAPES
Rack plates, teaplates, Windmill teaset, Tavern
jug, Ball teapot, child's beaker, Poyntz jug,
porridge plate, Leeds fruit dish, Pelican cup and
saucer, Rex mug, fruit saucer, unrecorded jug,
sugar castor, matchstriker

DATES
This series was introduced in 1902 and
withdrawn by 1932

Note Although mottoes appear with most scenes
in the pattern books, they rarely feature on
the wares

Pastimes. Rack plate, 36.

Pastimes. Porridge plate, 35.

Pastimes. Teapot, *top* 38, *bottom* 28.

Pastimes. Matchstriker, *top* 47, *bottom* 46.

Pastimes. Pattern book pages with original mottoes, *left top* 2, *bottom* 3, *right top* 16 and 17, *centre* 1, *bottom* 40 and 45.

Pastimes. *Left to right* 10, 12.

Pastimes. 14.

Pastimes. *Top, left to right* 18, 44 and 19, *bottom* 43.

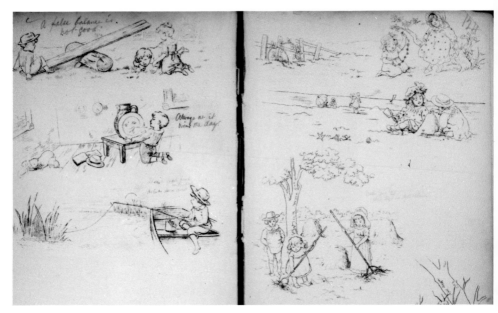

Pastimes. *Left to right, from top to bottom* 30, 39, 31, 38, 32, 33.

Pastimes. *Top, left to right* 6, 8, *bottom* 7, 9.

Pastimes. Porridge plate 13.

Pastimes. *Left to right, from top to bottom* 23, 37, 24, 27, 36, 28, 25, 29, 26.

Pastimes. *Top* 41, *bottom* 21.

Pastimes. *Top* 4, *bottom* 5.

Playtime. *Left to right, from top to bottom* 16, 17, 23, 9, 10, 19, 18, 11, 12, 20, 13, 24, 15, 21, 2, 14, 1, 22.

Playtime. Biscuit jar, *left to right* 1, 2.

Playtime
SCENES/TITLES
1 Boy and girl with picnic
2 Boy and girl building a dam on the beach
3 Babies fishing, maids watching
4 Girl fishing
5 Girl under umbrella
6 Girl gathering flowers
7 Boy fishing
8 Boy releasing bird from cage
9 Three children reading aloud
10 Three girls knitting
11 Girl sitting with dog
12 Girl and boy dancing
13 Girl standing under umbrella
14 Girl with doll's pram
15 Girl picking fruit
16 Two maids and two babies, one with doll
17 Girl sitting with basket of flowers

71

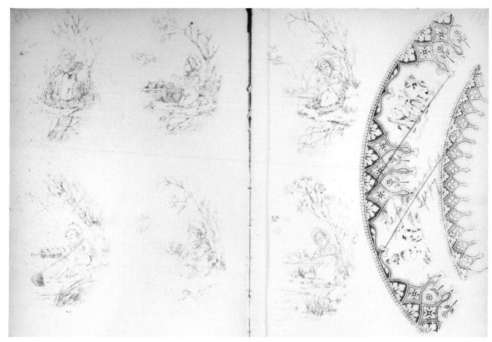

Playtime. *Top, left to right* 6, 8, 5, *bottom* 7, 8, 4.

18 Boy chasing hat
19 Boy and girl on beach
20 Girl skipping
21 Two girls, one with broken umbrella
22 Boy tying on girl's skates
23 Girl playing with doll
24 Girl standing with dog

PATTERN NUMBERS
D1239

BORDERS
Gold flowers

COLOURWAYS
Polychrome

SHAPES
Biscuit jar

DATES
This series was introduced in c 1890 and
withdrawn by World War I

Playtime. 3.

Sampler or Peter Pan. Rack plate, 1.

Sampler or Peter Pan

SCENES/TITLES
1 House with cows in foreground
2 Gable end of house
3 Facade of house, door left
4 Facade of house, door centre
5 View of house through archway

PATTERN NUMBERS
D3749, D3753

COLOURWAYS
Polychrome

SHAPES
Plate, Westcott jug, Lennox flower bowl, Corinth teaset, Mayfair toilet set, Regent fern bowl, Peary ice jug, tea caddy, Reflex baby plate, Leeds porridge bowl, Marcella tobacco jar, Pelican trinket set and candlestick, Rex mug, Ancestor ashtray, Empire cup and saucer, Leeds fruit saucer, Leeds oatmeal saucer, York sandwich tray, vase numbers 6886, 7012, 7014, 7016, 7017, 7018, 7023, 7346, 7347, 7350, 7352, 7386, 7388, 7429, 7432, 7444, 7465, 7493, 7506, 7507, 7531, 7532, 7533

DATES
This series was introduced in 1924 and withdrawn by 1936

SPECIAL BACKSTAMP

Sampler or Peter Pan. Publicity photograph featuring 2, 3, 4 and 5.

Seaside. 3.

Seaside
SCENES/TITLES
1 Girls building sandcastle
2 Boy with fishing net
3 Boy with wheelbarrow

PATTERN NUMBERS
D3298

COLOURWAYS
Polychrome

SHAPES
Plates, unrecorded jug

DATES
This series was introduced in 1910 and withdrawn by 1914

Seaside. Jug, 1.

Seaside. Jug, 2.

Springtime. Rack plates, *top, left to right* 9 and 10, 11 and 1, *centre* 7, *bottom* 5 and 4, 3 and 6.

Springtime. 2.

Springtime. Matchstriker, 13 and 8.

Springtime

CHARACTERS
1 Two girls hand in hand, and an older girl with cloak
2 Girl holding dress out with both hands, another curtseying
3 Three girls, one pulling another's dress bow
4 Procession of six girls
5 Profile of girl holding cloak
6 Two girls in cloaks dancing, one holding flower
7 Two girls in cloaks, one dancing, the other playing horn
8 Two girls in short dresses dancing arm in arm
9 One girl in short dress holding a flower and dancing
10 Procession of eight girls
11 Two girls, one with flower
12 Similar to number 7 but with other girl playing horn
13 Girl curtseying

PATTERN NUMBERS
D3119

COLOURWAYS
Polychrome

SHAPES
Rack plates, candlestick number 7227, Dutch candlestick, teapot A, Westcott jug, stein, vase number 7275, matchstriker, tobacco jar, Lagoon toilet set

DATES
This series was introduced in 1909 and withdrawn by 1932

Tobogganing A
SCENES/TITLES
1 Broken toboggan, three boys on board
2 Snowball fight between toboggan passengers

Springtime. Stein, 12.

Tobogganing A. 3.

Tobogganing A. 6.

3 Two boys tobogganing downhill, third
  passenger falling in snow – 'Good heed doth
  surely speed'
4 Three boys on toboggan in the path of
  another approaching
5 Three boys on toboggan chased by dog
6 Four boys about to fall off toboggan

PATTERN NUMBERS
D2955, D2956, D2979

BORDERS
Greek key and stylised flowers, fir tree

COLOURWAYS
Polychrome, Holbein, blue

SHAPES
Plates, Concord jug, loving cup number 7058,
miniatures

DATES
This series was introduced in 1908 and
withdrawn by 1928

Tobogganing A. Rack plate, 2.

Tobogganing A. Rack plates, *left to right* 4, 5, 1.

Toboganing B.
Pages from pattern
book.

Toboganing B

These scenes of various winter sports are
featured in the pattern book beside
Toboganing A and may be an extension of this
series or they may not have been produced at
all as no pattern numbers have been recorded

Victorian Tile Murals. Plates, *left to right, top* 1, 2, 3, *bottom* 4, 5, 6.

Victorian Tile Murals
SCENES/TITLES
1 Feeding time
2 The Milking Lesson
3 Maytime
4 Apple Gathering
5 Gleaning
6 Gathering Firewood

BORDERS
Scrolls

COLOURWAYS
Polychrome

SHAPES
Wall plates

DATES
This series of six plates was introduced in pairs from 1982 – 1985 to raise money for the Charing Cross Medical Research Centre Appeal

DESIGNER
Alan Carr Linford from the Victorian tile murals at Charing Cross Hospital

SPECIAL BACKSTAMP giving details of the limited edition of 1,500

Nursery Rhymes

Nursery rhymes have been the most fertile source of imagery for Doulton designers of children's china. No less than forty-seven favourite rhymes have been recorded, many in several versions, in fifteen different series. From the early 1900s until the Second World War this was undoubtedly the most popular way to enliven children's mealtimes.

The term "nursery rhyme" first appeared in the 1830s. Prior to that the verses were known as "Tommy Thumb's Songs" or "Mother Goose's Songs" – the name still used in the USA. Most nursery rhymes are heard for the first time on mother's knee where they are either said or sung to soothe or amuse. They have been associated with childhood for so long that it is perhaps surprising to learn that the majority were not originally composed for young ears. Many are survivals of old folk songs and some, in their original wording, would have been highly unsuitable for the nursery. The bawdy jokes and strong language were censored from drinking ditties and love ballads when the rhymes first went into print for children but in the nineteenth century there was still some concern about the unsavoury element which remained; in particular, the cruelty and violence. However, gory tales have persisted well into the twentieth century with little thought given to the words or their origin – for example the plight of the three blind mice whose tails were cut off with a carving knife!

Some of the rhymes are believed to refer to real people such as Jack Horner who was steward to the Abbot of Glastonbury at the time of the dissolution of the monasteries. In the hope of appeasing King Henry VIII, Jack Horner was sent with a Christmas gift of a pie which contained the title deeds of twelve manors. Jack apparently pulled out the "plum" for himself – the Manor of Mells where descendants of the Horner family still live today.

Few nursery rhymes have such a plausible explanation – indeed some are just plain nonsense such as the fantastic imagery and lyrics in *Hey diddle diddle* where "the cow jumped

over the moon" and "the dish ran away with the spoon". This surreal scenario is one of nineteen rhymes portrayed by William Savage Cooper in Royal Doulton's first nursery rhymes series, introduced in 1903 and not withdrawn until the outbreak of World War Two. Queen Alexandra ordered this nursery design for use by her grandchildren so no doubt this royal stamp of approval added to its popularity. In 1905 a forty piece teaset was advertised for £1.50 so obviously Royal Doulton were still catering for very large families.

The other early nursery ware series do not seem to have commanded the same attention or sales, judging by their scarcity in the market place today. Most surprisingly no pieces have yet been found featuring *My Pretty Maid* by the "Lord of the Nursery", Randolph Caldecott, which suggests it did not sell as well as expected.

Few of the original illustrators of the nursery rhymes can be identified with any certainty. The monogram φ found on *Nursery Rhymes F* is possibly J. Ogden, a painter and illustrator who was exhibiting in London earlier this century. The characters portrayed in *Nursery Rhymes L*, which was very popular between the wars, are in the style of Ann Anderson and her imitators. In the drawings for *Nursery Rhymes B and C*, the Burslem artists have clearly been influenced by their Lambeth colleagues William Rowe and Margaret Thompson who designed tile murals for children's wards in hospitals. It may even be that Miss Thompson, who was also a book illustrator in her spare time, actually drew the illustrations for the nursery tableware as they are very close to her tiles.

These hospital murals have recently been re-interpreted by Neil Faulkner in the latest nursery rhyme series (N) and there is every indication that these will be as popular with children today as the murals were in their original setting.

Nursery Rhymes A – Savage Cooper. Plates 6, 5, 2, 13, 15, 18, 14.

Nursery Rhymes A – Savage Cooper. Plate, bowl and mug, *left to right* 8, 7, 1.

Nursery Rhymes A – Savage Cooper. Cups and saucers, *left to right* 16, 18, 19, 10.

Nursery Rhymes A – Savage Cooper. Plate, 9.

Nursery Rhymes A – Savage Cooper. Rack plate, 17.

Nursery Rhymes A – Savage Cooper. Beaker, teapot and jug, *left to right* 3, 12, 4.

Nursery Rhymes A – Savage Cooper. Mugs and beaker, *left to right* 11, 8, 2.

Nursery Rhymes A – Savage Cooper
SCENES/TITLES
1 There was an old woman who lived in a shoe
2 Old Mother Goose
3 Hey diddle diddle, the cat and the fiddle
4 To market, to market, to buy a fat pig
5 Old Mother Hubbard went to the cupboard
6 Ride a cock horse to Banbury Cross
7 Simple Simon met a pieman going to the fair
8 Little Bo Peep has lost her sheep
9 Little Tom Tucker sang for his supper
10 There was a little man and he had a little gun
11 Where are you going to my pretty maid?
12 Peter Piper picked a peck of pickled peppers
13 Mary, Mary quite contrary

14 Jack and the beanstalk
15 The Queen of Hearts
16 Little Boy Blue
17 Little Red Riding Hood
18 Old King Cole was a merry old soul
19 This is the house that Jack built

Occasionally two scenes are featured on one item

PATTERN NUMBER
D1811, D1817, D1870, D1871, D3606, D5187, E1441, E3255

BORDERS
Hearts with thistles, roses and shamrocks in relief, gold, stylised leaves, fruit and foliage

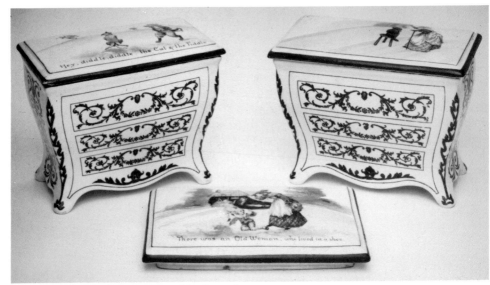

Nursery Rhymes A – Savage Cooper. Huntley and Palmer biscuit caskets, *left to right* 3, 1, 5.

COLOURWAYS
Polychrome

SHAPES
Plates, Burke beakers, Clayton jug, Cecil teacup and saucer, bowl, mugs, eggcup and saucer, Leeds fruit dish, Huntley and Palmer biscuit jar, Reflex baby plate, unrecorded tureen, tray numbers 598 and 657

DATES
This series was introduced in 1903 and withdrawn by 1939

DESIGNER
William Savage Cooper (1863–1943)

Note This series was ordered by Queen Alexandra for use by her grandchildren

Nursery Rhymes B
SCENES/TITLES
1 Old King Cole
2 Little Bo Peep
3 Little Jack Horner
4 Jack and Jill
5 Mary, Mary quite contrary
6 Little Boy Blue
7 See Saw Margery Daw
8 Hark, hark the dogs do bark
9 Baa Baa Black Sheep have you any wool

PATTERN NUMBERS
D1531, D2515, D3082, D3083

SHAPES
Baby plate

COLOURWAYS
Polychrome

DATES
This series was introduced in 1903 and withdrawn by 1930

Nursery Rhymes B. Baby plate, 9.

Nursery Rhymes B. Baby plate, 7.

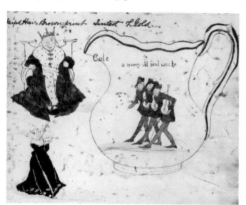

Nursery Rhymes B. Jug, 1.

Nursery Rhymes B. Saucer, 8.

Nursery Rhymes C. Mug, 6.

Note This series of nursery rhymes and the next one are obviously influenced by Doulton's hospital tile murals designed by Margaret Thompson and William Rowe and painted at the Lambeth studio between 1901 and World War I

Nursery Rhymes B. *Left to right, from top to bottom* 1,
6, 2, 8, 5, 7, 3, 4, 9.

Nursery Rhymes C. Baby plate, 2.

Nursery Rhymes C

SCENES/TITLES
1 Baa Baa Black Sheep have you any wool
2 Little Miss Muffet
3 Jack and Jill
4 Little Red Riding Hood
5 Old King Cole
6 Here we go gathering nuts in May
7 Little Bo Peep
8 Mary, Mary quite contrary
9 See Saw Margery Daw
10 Little Boy Blue
11 Simple Simon went a fishing
12 Hark, hark, the dogs do bark, the beggars
have come to town

PATTERN NUMBERS
D3083

BORDERS
Stylised leaves

COLOURWAYS
Polychrome

SHAPES
Rack plate, baby plate, Rheims teacup and
saucer, mug, oatmeal saucer

Nursery Rhymes C.
*Left to right, from top
to bottom* 5, 12, 1,
11, 7, 6, 2, 4, 3.

DATES
This series was introduced in 1909 and
withdrawn by 1930

Note It would appear that scenes from this
series merged with Nursery Rhymes B as the
number D3083 has also been recorded on the
earlier *Old King Cole* illustration

Nursery Rhymes D – Jack and Jill
SCENES/TITLES
1 Jack and Jill went up the hill to fetch a pail of
water – 'The pleasure of doing good is the
only one that never wears out' and 'Nothing
is troublesome that we do willingly'
2 Jack and Jill holding a bucket of water
3 Jack and Jill tumbling down

PATTERN NUMBERS
D1712, D1713, D1714

COLOURWAYS
Polychrome, sepia, blue and white

SHAPES
Tavern jug

DATES
This series was introduced in 1903 and
withdrawn by 1930

Nursery Rhymes D – Jack and Jill. Jug, 1.

Nursery Rhymes D – Jack and Jill. *Left to right, top* 1, 3, *bottom* 2.

Nursery Rhymes E – My Pretty Maid. Original illustrations by Randolph Caldecott.

Nursery Rhymes E – My Pretty Maid. 2.

Nursery Rhymes E – My Pretty Maid

SCENES/TITLES
1 Where are you going my pretty maid?
   I'm going a milking sir she said
2 Shall I go with you my pretty maid?
   Oh yes if you please kind sir she said
3 Will you marry me my pretty maid?
   Thank you kindly sir she said

4 But what is your fortune my pretty maid?
   My face is my fortune sir she said
5 Then I can't marry you my pretty maid
   Nobody asked you sir she said
6 I must be going my pretty maid

PATTERN NUMBERS
D2404, D2579

BORDERS
Flowers

COLOURWAYS
Polychrome, Whieldon

SHAPES
Friar teapot, biscuit box

DATES
This series was introduced in 1905 and
withdrawn by 1930

DESIGNER
These scenes were based on illustrations by
Randolph Caldecott for *The Milkmaid* picture
book published in 1882

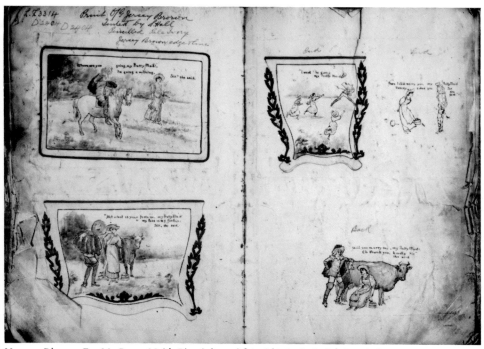

Nursery Rhymes E – My Pretty Maid. Biscuit box, *left to right, top* 1, 6, 5, *bottom* 4, 3.

Nursery Rhymes F. Rack plates, *left to right, top* 3, 11, *centre* 12, *bottom* 1, 2.

Nursery Rhymes F. 7.

Nursery Rhymes F. 6.

Nursery Rhymes F. Rack plates, *left to right* 9, 8.

Nursery Rhymes F. *Left to right* 5, 4.

DATES
This series was introduced in 1906 and withdrawn by 1930

DESIGNER
J. Ogden

Nursery Rhymes F

SCENES/TITLES
1 The Pied Piper of Hamelin
2 Little Miss Muffet
3 To market, to market to buy a fat pig
4 Little Tom Tucker
5 I love little pussy
6 Little Jack Horner
7 Baby Bunting
8 Baa Baa Black Sheep
9 Where are you going to my pretty maid?
10 Little Bo Peep
11 Tom the piper's son
12 Old King Cole

PATTERN NUMBERS
D2534, D2539, D2540, D2921, D2922

BORDERS
Greek key, stylised flowers

COLOURWAYS
Polychrome, blue and white

SHAPES
Rack plates

Nursery Rhymes F. 10.

Nursery Rhymes G – Toys. Baby plate, 3.

Nursery Rhymes G – Toys. Baby plates, 2.

Nursery Rhymes G – Toys. Jug and mug *left to right,* 1, 4.

Nursery Rhymes G – Toys

SCENES/TITLES
1 Three blind mice see how they run
2 There was a little man and he had a little gun
3 Rock a bye baby on a tree top
4 Little Miss Muffet sat on a tuffet

PATTERN NUMBERS
D2833, D4016

BORDERS
Toys and trees

COLOURWAYS
Polychrome, black and white

SHAPES
Plate, round baby plate, Poyntz jug, Lagoon toilet set, Reflex baby plate

DATES
This series was introduced in 1907 and withdrawn by 1934

Nursery Rhymes H – The Man in the Moon

SCENES/TITLES
Profile of man in the moon against stars and clouds

PATTERN NUMBERS
Not recorded

COLOURWAYS
Holbein

SHAPES
Rack plate

DATES
The date 1907 appears on the only recorded plate. It was probably withdrawn by 1914

Note Several different nursery rhymes refer to the old folk-lore of the man in the moon

92

Nursery Rhymes I – Polly put the kettle on.
Teapot.

Nursery Rhymes I – Polly Put the Kettle On
SCENES/TITLES
Dancing girls

PATTERN NUMBERS
D1909

COLOURWAYS
Polychrome

SHAPES
Teapot

DATES
The series was introduced in 1904 and
withdrawn by 1932

Nursery Rhymes J – Baa Baa Black Sheep. Mug
and baby plate.

Nursery Rhymes J – Baa Baa Black Sheep
SCENES/TITLES
Silhouette farmer with bags of wool and sheep

PATTERN NUMBERS
D3312, D3330, D3357

COLOURWAYS
Black and ochre, black and red, black and gold

SHAPES
Baby plate and mug

DATES
This series was introduced in 1910 and
withdrawn by 1930

Nursery Rhymes H – The Man in the Moon.
Rack plate.

Nursery Rhymes K. *Left to right, top* 11, 10, 1, 2, *centre* 4, 12, 9, 8, 7, 6, 3, *bottom* 9, 8, 12, 5, 11.

Nursery Rhymes K
SCENES/TITLES
1 Jack and Jill went up the hill
2 Little Boy Blue come blow up your horn
3 Little Tom Tucker sang for his supper
4 Simple Simon met a pieman going to the fair
5 See Saw Margery Daw
6 Queen of Hearts she made some tarts
7 Where are you going my pretty maid?
8 Little Bo Peep has lost her sheep
9 Little Miss Muffet sat on a tuffet
10 Ring a ring of roses, a pocket full of posies
11 Little Jack Horner sat in the corner
12 Mary, Mary quite contrary, how does your garden grow?

PATTERN NUMBERS
D3918

COLOURWAYS
Polychrome

SHAPES
Jug

DATES
This series was introduced in 1915 and withdrawn by 1934

Nursery Rhymes K. Jug, 2.

Nursery Rhymes K. 1.

Nursery Rhymes L

SCENES/TITLES
1 This little pig
2 Little Tommy Tucker sings for his supper
3 Hush a bye baby on the tree top
4 Sing a song of sixpence
5 Jack and Jill
6 Little Bo Peep has lost her sheep
7 Simple Simon went a fishing
8 Oranges and lemons
9 Polly put the kettle on
10 The Queen of Hearts she made some tarts
11 Goosey Goosey Gander
12 Little Miss Muffet

PATTERN NUMBERS
D4063, D4064, D4083, H724, H768, H769

BORDERS
Fruit, birds, plain band border

COLOURWAYS
Polychrome

SHAPES
Plates, Rex mug, silver plated eggcup and stand,
Cecil teacup and saucer, baby plate, baby mug,
porridge plate, Burke beaker with silver handle,
plain beaker, Rheims cup, 5" plate, 6" plate,
7" plate

DATES
This series was introduced in 1916 and
withdrawn by 1940

DESIGNER
In the style of Ann Anderson

Nursery Rhymes L. Cups and Saucers *left to right* 8, 3, 6, 4.

Nursery Rhymes L. Plates, *left to right, from top to bottom* 5, 9, 10, 12, 11, 1, 11.

Nursery Rhymes L. Plate, 6.

Nursery Rhymes L. Cup and saucer, porridge plate and mug, *left to right* 7, 8, 5, 8.

Nursery Rhymes L. Beaker, eggcup and mug, *left to right* 7, 2.

Nursery Rhymes M – Cock A Doodle Do. Plate and mug, *left to right* 2, 6.

Nursery Rhymes M – Cock A Doodle Do. Baby plate, cup and mug, *left to right, top* 3, 3, 7, *bottom* 4.

Nursery Rhymes M – Cock A Doodle Do

SCENES/TITLES
1 Rooster on fence crowing, boy collecting eggs
2 Girl feeding hens
3 Rooster crowing beside pond
4 Three hens walking past duck pond
5 Hen laying an egg
6 Two ducks running into the pond
7 Three ducks swimming

PATTERN NUMBERS
D4686, D4830

COLOURWAYS
Polychrome

SHAPES
Rack plates, teaplates, Westcott jug, baby plate, Cleveland teaset, Rex mug, Harlech teacup and saucer, bowl, Jeff cream jug, beaker

DATES
This series was introduced in 1928 and withdrawn by 1939

SPECIAL BACKSTAMP

Nursery Rhymes M
– Cock A Doodle
Do. *Top 5, bottom 1.*

Nursery Rhymes N – Tile Murals

SCENES/TITLES
1 See Saw Margery Daw
2 Little Boy Blue
3 Nuts an' May
4 Little Bo Peep

BORDERS
Floral

COLOURWAYS
Polychrome

SHAPES
Wall plates

DATES
This series was introduced in 1986 to raise money for the rescue of the tile murals at Wellington Hospital, New Zealand

DESIGNER
Neil Faulkner from the Doulton tile murals at St Thomas's Hospital, London and the Wellington Hospital, New Zealand

SPECIAL BACKSTAMP

Nursery Rhymes O
See section on miniatures

Nursery Rhymes N. Tile murals, 1, 2, 3, 4.

Miniatures

Toy was the name used in the eighteenth century to describe a miniature version of a familiar household object, created for the amusement of adults. Ladies of leisure would delight in arranging their tiny treasures in display cabinets or furnishing dolls' houses, for these were not then the preserve of the young. The little objects were fashioned in bronze, silver or ceramic, not by professional toymakers but by the appropriate specialist craftsmen. Thus the Chelsea, Worcester and Caughley factories made minute teasets in porcelain and exquisite examples were also imported from China and Europe.

The Victorians were equally fascinated by the diminutive and avidly read the tales of Gulliver in Lilliput and the adventures of Tom Thumb. They too could create a world in miniature in their drawing rooms, helped by firms such as Doulton who offered tiny versions of their famous products. All the popular decorative techniques of the Lambeth studio were represented on a reduced scale – Hunting wares, Silicon wares, simulated Leather and Copper wares and of course, the traditional salt glazed stonewares with applied rosettes and beading. There are vases, bowls, jugs, loving cups and even plain bottles, some less than an inch in height. It is thought that some of these ingenious little pieces were designed as travellers' samples but their frequency in the marketplace indicates that they must have had a wider circulation.

It is possible that some of the tiniest pieces were originally sold as dolls' house furnishings. In the early 1920s Royal Doulton helped equip one of the country's most famous dolls' houses which was presented by the nation to Queen Mary and is now exhibited at Windsor Castle. The Lambeth studio created storage jars and cooking wares for the kitchen, all to the required scale of one twelfth normal size and the Burslem studio contributed a perfectly executed bone china dinner service with plates only half an inch in diameter adorned with the Royal monogram. Despite their obvious

technical expertise in this scale, the Burslem potters did not specialise in dolls' house furniture or even the slightly larger toy teasets for dolls' nursery parties. Some of the most popular tableware patterns such as *Willow, Norfolk, Blue Iris* and other floral sprays were "shrunk" but it seems more likely that these were intended for collectors rather than as playthings.

Collecting miniature china was a widespread hobby at the beginning of the century judging by Royal Doulton's advertisement in *The Queen* magazine of 1905. "To the miniature china collector (and who today is not?) this idea will prove specially welcome". The "idea" was a ceramic alternative to Christmas cards in the form of tiny vases, jugs or loving cups, portraying Santa Claus and appropriate seasonal mottoes, which were sold complete with postal box. It was not a new notion as Moore Brothers of Longton had already offered similar novelties. Royal Doulton believed that it would become "a fairly general method of sending good wishes" as the miniatures only cost one shilling, which was apparently the cost of the average good quality Christmas card and the postage was only a penny. Despite the attractive price the idea of china greetings does not seem to have caught on. Undaunted, Royal Doulton continued to use the twenty different little shapes they had developed but marketed them differently. Seasonal imagery continued to be popular and the Christmas goose and turkey with holly and mistletoe appear on a variety of miniatures. The delightful series *Snowflake*, featuring sheep or goats in the snow, has also been associated with the festive season as has the *Skating* series (see Volume 2).

The subject matter was not confined to Christmas, however. Nearly fifty different patterns have been recorded in miniature including some of the most popular such as *Dickens, Coaching Days, Jackdaw of Rheims,* and *Under the Greenwood Tree*. Most of the pieces range from one to three inches in height and, as well as the standard vases and jugs, unusual

Christmas – Santa Claus. Loving cup and teapot, *left to right* 4, 3.

Christmas – Santa Claus. Jug and vase, 6, 2.

shapes such as coal scuttles, teapots and trays were offered. Some of the shapes could also be functional. The little flasks with silver lids were probably for perfume and several of the vases could be used as toothpick holders. Prices were modest. According to the trade circular of 1905, the price of a dozen assorted items was reduced to four shillings because there was "a real want for a sixpenny line of miniatures". Now of course they command considerable sums of money and are extremely sought after. The reasons are not hard to see. A representative collection can be housed in one cabinet, creating minimum demands on space and collectors can enjoy the delights of Series ware in microcosm.

Christmas – Santa Claus
SCENES/TITLES
1 Santa on sleigh drawn by reindeer
2 Santa going down chimney
3 Santa holding balloons in front of sleigh
4 Santa filling stockings
5 Santa carrying sack
6 Santa with balloons and toys

Christmas – Santa Claus. *Top to bottom* 2, 6, 5, 4.

PATTERN NUMBERS
E2440, E2806, E4109, E5108

BORDERS
Mistletoe, holly

COLOURWAYS
Polychrome

SHAPES
Miniature vases, jugs, loving cups and teapots
and small plates, teacups and saucers

DATES
This series was introduced in 1904 and
withdrawn by 1914

Note Seasonal quotations are found on some of
the miniatures, for example:
'Tobacco and a good coal fire are things this
season doth require'
'Now trees their leafy hats do bare to
reverence winter's silvery hair'

Christmas Fare. Jugs, *top* 1, *bottom* 2.

Christmas Fare
SCENES/TITLES
1 Turkey
2 Geese

Holly and mistletoe on reverse

PATTERN NUMBERS
E2440

COLOURWAYS
Polychrome

SHAPES
Miniature vases and jugs

DATES
This series was introduced in 1904 and
withdrawn by 1914

Christmas – Santa Claus. Fluted dish, 1.

WITH SANTA CLAUS SUBJECTS IN ENAMEL COLOURS ON PORCELAIN.

Each little Vase is decorated with one of the above mentioned subjects
and mottoes; also with a border of Christmas Bells or Holly and
the handle and edge is finished in solid Sèvres Green.

Christmas miniatures advertisement 1905.

Nursery Rhymes O. Jug, 7.

Nursery Rhymes O

SCENES/TITLES
1 There was an old woman who lived in a shoe
2 Old Mother Hubbard she went to the cupboard
3 Ride a cock horse to Banbury Cross
4 Little Boy Blue come blow your horn
5 Little Bo Peep has lost her sheep
6 There was a little man and he had a little gun
7 Where are you going to my pretty maid?
8 Little Jack Horner
9 Jack and Jill went up the hill
10 A dillar, a dollar, a ten o'clock scholar
11 Jack Spratt could eat no fat, his wife could eat no lean
12 Tom, Tom the Piper's son
13 Peter Piper picked a peck of pickled peppers
14 Simple Simon met a pieman going to the fair
15 Pat a cake, pat a cake bakers man
16 Ding dong bell, pussy's in the well
17 A ring a ring of roses, a pocket full of posies
18 Little Tom Tucker sang for his supper

PATTERN NUMBERS
E5773

COLOURWAYS
Polychrome

SHAPES
Miniature jugs

DATES
This series was introduced in 1907 and withdrawn by 1932

Silhouettes

SCENES/TITLES
1 'He who calmly smokes thinks like a sage and acts like a samaritan'
2 'Rest to the weary to the hungry food, the last kind refuge of the wise and good'
3 'Tobacco I would do anything but die for thy sake'
4 'When all things were made none were made better than tobacco'

Nursery Rhymes O.
Top to bottom 13, 12, 11, 8, 9, 10, 2, 8.

Nursery Rhymes O. *Top to bottom* 4, 3, 5, 1.

Nursery Rhymes O. *Top to bottom* 15, 14, 16, 17, 6, 18.

CHARACTERS
Various characters cut from one long transfer.

PATTERN NUMBERS
E2275

BORDERS
Jacobean

COLOURWAYS
Black and red, black and yellow, black and blue, red, Holbein

SHAPES
Miniature jugs, vases, loving cups and teapots and small plates, trays and Tavern jug

DATES
This series was introduced in 1904 and withdrawn by 1930

DESIGNER
J. Ogden

Snowflake
SCENES/TITLES
1 A herd of goats in snow
2 A flock of sheep in snow

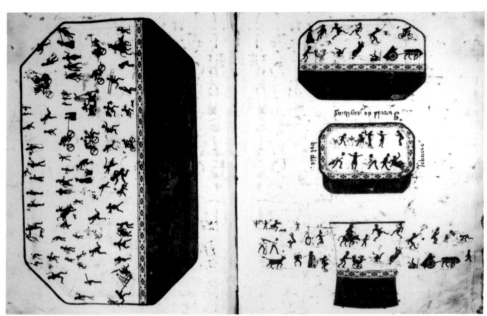

Silhouettes. *Left* 1, *right, top to bottom* 4, 3, 2.

Silhouettes. Pattern book page.

Snowflake. Vases, *left to right*, 2, 1.

BORDERS
Trees and landscapes

COLOURWAYS
Polychrome

SHAPES
Miniature vases, jugs, loving cups, bone china
cup and saucer

DATES
This series was introduced in 1904 and
withdrawn by 1914

PATTERN NUMBERS
E2653, E2690, E4487, E5097

Various Series in Miniature

To date the following Series ware patterns have
been recorded in miniature:
Alice in Wonderland – Vol 3
All Black Cricketers – Vol 3
Arabs and Camels – Vol 4
Bateman – Vol 1
Bobbie Burns B – Vol 1
Caldecott A – Vol 1
Castles – Vol 1
Christmas – Santa Claus – Vol 3
Christmas Fare – Vol 3
Churches – Vol 1
Coaching Days – Vol 2

Cotswold Shepherd – Vol 2
Dickens A – Vol 1
English Cottages – Vol 2
Gaffers – Vol 2
Gallant Fishers – Vol 2
Gleaners – Vol 2
Golfers – Vol 2
Gondoliers – Vol 4
Harlem – Vol 4
Historic Towns – Vol 1
Hunting, John Peel – Vol 2
Isle of Man – Vol 2
Izaak Walton – Vol 1
Jackdaw of Rheims – Vol 1
Nursery Rhymes – Vol 3
Persian – Vol 4
Roger de Coverley – Vol 1
Santa Claus – Vol 3
Shakespeare G – Vol 1
Silhouettes – Vol 3
Skating – Vol 2
Snowflake – Vol 3
Under the Greenwood Tree – Vol 1
Welsh – Vol 2
Zunday Smocks – Vol 2

The following tableware patterns have also been
recorded:
Blue Iris
Daisies
Norfolk
Watteau
Willow
Rose sprays, violet sprays and various other
flower patterns

MISCELLANEOUS
The imp from Lincoln Cathedral
Royal Commemoratives
Various city crests and national
commemoratives
Sunset scene
Rabbits

SHAPES
Plates, vases, jugs, loving cups, teapots, mugs,
trays, buckets, coal scuttles, toothpick holders,
patch or pill boxes, cauldron, perfume bottles

Skaters. (See Series Ware Volume 2)

Dutch. (See Series Ware Volume 4)

Charmingly-drawn
Animals in Snow,
with glowing red
sunset skies.

ROYAL DOULTON CHINA "SNOWFLAKE" WARE

Snowflake. Catalogue page.

108

Pattern and Code Numbers & Date Guide

The following tables of numbers indicate the approximate periods when the first relevant patterns so numbered were first *introduced*. Many patterns were in production over a number of years, carrying the same pattern numbers, and so the numbers cannot be used to establish the date of manufacture. This can be established either from the style of the backstamps, or from the impressed date code if present – normally the last two figures of the year preceded by a number indicating the month, for example 10.08 means a manufacturing date of October 1908. However, unless date codes are present, it is generally impossible to establish precise dates of manufacture for Series wares. In the tables below, A and D numbers indicate earthenware patterns, while E and H were used for fine china.

A Numbers

Pattern number	Date of introduction
1 – 6882	c. 1881 – 1892
6883 – 7467	1893
7468 – 8084	1894
8085 – 8592	1895
8593 – 9144	1896
9145 – 9617	1897
9618 – 10000	1898

D Numbers

Pattern number	Date of introduction
1 – 339	1899
340 – 769	1900
770 – 1137	1901
1138 – 1495	1902
1496 – 1869	1903
1870 – 2161	1904
2162 – 2442	1905
2443 – 2723	1906
2724 – 2914	1907
2915 – 3079	1908
3080 – 3229	1909
3230 – 3374	1910
3375 – 3519	1911
3520 – 3635	1912
3636 – 3714	1913
3715 – 3821	1914
3822 – 3939	1915
3940 – 4074	1916 – 1918
4075 – 4143	1919 – 1920
4144 – 4230	1921 – 1922
4231 – 4360	1923
4361 – 4470	1924
4471 – 4559	1925
4560 – 4659	1926
4660 – 4737	1927
4738 – 4822	1928
4823 – 4969	1929
4970 – 5069	1930
5070 – 5169	1931
5170 – 5230	1932
5231 – 5429	1933
5430 – 5520	1934
5521 – 5612	1935
5613 – 5749	1936
5750 – 5875	1937
5876 – 6009	1938
6010 – 6110	1939
6111 – 6285	1940 – 1948
6286 – 6390	1949 – 1952
6391 – 6408	1953
6409 – 6438	1954
6439 – 6454	1955
6455 – 6464	1956
6465 – 6492	1957
6493 – 6507	1958
6508 – 6547	1959
6548 – 6558	1960
6559 – 6567	1961
6568 – 6587	1962
6588 – 6596	1963
6597 – 6606	1964

E Numbers

Pattern number	Date of introduction
1 – 940	1901 – 1902
941 – 1950	1903
1951 – 3040	1904
3041 – 4054	1905 – 1906
4055 – 6015	1907 – 1910
6016 – 7863	1911
7684 – 8277	1912
8278 – 8933	1913
8934 – 9527	1914
9528 – 10000	1915

H Numbers

Pattern number	Date of introduction
1 – 359	1916
360 – 709	1917
710 – 759	1918
760 – 906	1919
907 – 1049	1920
1050 – 1179	1921
1180 – 1443	1922
1444 – 1812	1923
1813 – 2268	1924
2269 – 2649	1925
2650 – 3180	1926
3181 – 3599	1927
3600 – 3770	1928
3771 – 3909	1929
3910 – 4010	1930
4011 – 4099	1931
4100 – 4189	1932
4190 – 4240	1933
4241 – 4329	1934
4330 – 4425	1935
4426 – 4519	1936
4520 – 4609	1937
4610 – 4710	1938
4711 – 4821	1939 – 1942
4822 – 4849	1943 – 1946
4850 – 4906	1947 – 1952
4907 – 4930	1953
4931 – 4935	1954
4936 – 4941	1955
4942 – 4950	1956 – 1957
4951 – 4956	1958
4957 – 4959	1959
4960 – 4961	1960
4962 – 4964	1961
4965 – 4968	1962
4969 – 4975	1963

Index